INTERSTELLAR MAP
OF PREVIOUS YEAR'S
TRAVELLING

PROPOSED ROUTE

**INTENDED CO-ORDINATES
AT YEAR END**

348,543.4
AA3.2

SPACE FACTS
MIMAS

Large settlements on south side.
Site of Space Corps test base.
Popular supply centre and
stop-off point.

Data Table

MIMAS	Lat.°	Long.°
Craters		
Bedivere	10 N	145
Bors	45 N	165
Gwynevere	12 S	312
Launcelot	10 S	317
Morgan	25 N	240
Chasmata		
Avalon	20-57 N	160-120
Oeta	10-35 N	130-105
Ossa	10-30 S	305-280

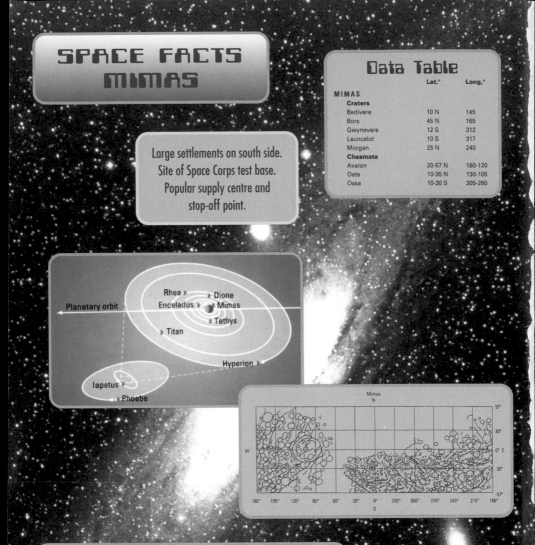

Satellites of Saturn

Name	Distance from Saturn, km	Orbital period, days	Orbital incl.,°	Orbital ecc.	Diameter, km	Mean opp. mag
Pan	133,600	0.57	0	0	20?	20?
Atlas	137,670	0.602	0.3	0.002	37 x 34 x 27	18.1
Prometheus	139,350	0.613	0.8	0.004	48 x 100 x 68	16.5
Pandora	141,700	0.629	0.1	0.004	110 x 88 x 62	16.3
Epimetheus	151,420	0.694	0.3	0.009	194 x 190 x 154	14.5
Janus	151,470	0.695	0.1	0.007	138 x 110 x 110	15.5
Mimas	185,540	0.942	1.52	0.020	194 x 190 x 154	12.9
Enceladus	238,040	1.370	0.07	0.004	421 x 395 x 395	11.8
Tethys	294,670	1.888	1.86	0.000	1046	10.3
Telesto	294,670	1.888	2	0	30 x 25 x 15	19.0
Calypso	294,670	1.888	2	0	30 x 16 x16	18.5
Dione	377,420	2.737	0.02	0.002	1120	10.4
Helene	377,420	2.737	0.2	0.005	35	18.5
Rhea	527,040	4.518	0.35	0.001	1528	9.7
Titan	1,221,860	15.495	0.33	0.029	5150	8.4
Hyperion	1,481,100	21.277	0.43	0.104	360 x 280 x 225	14.2
Iapetus	3,561,300	79.331	7.52	0.028	1436	10 (var)
Phoebe	12,954,000	550.4	175	0.163	30 x 220 x 210	16.5

RED DWARF ™

LOG No. 1996

Official Log For The Year:

SMEG KNOWS

Serving Crew: 1,167 4

HEINEMANN : LONDON

TECHNICAL INFORMATION
RED DWARF LOG No.1996

First published in Great Britain 1995
by William Heinemann Ltd
an imprint of Reed International Books Ltd
Michelin House, 81 Fulham Road, London SW3 6RB
and Auckland, Melbourne, Singapore and Toronto

Written by Paul Alexander
Researchers: Andrew Burnett and Sharon Burnett

Designed by Blackjacks
Colour reproduction by Scanners

Picture Credits
Front cover photograph © Mike Vaughan
Paul Grant – title page; 6 May; 1 August; 2, 23 September;
17 October; 15 November
Mike Vaughan – 2, 9, 19 January; 9, 12 February; 8, 27 April;
13, 28 May; 17 June; 22 July; 16 August; 2, 19 September; 31 October;
20 December; 2 January
Warwick Bedford/BBC – 4 March
Nobby Clark – 7 March
Oliver Upton – 6,10 June; 23 May; 28 October
Royal Observatory, Edinburgh/SPL – front star map
Francis Leroy, Biocosmos/SPL – rear star map
NASA/SPL – space facts background

A CIP catalogue record for this title is available from the British Library

ISBN 0 434 00370 0

Printed and bound by Jarrold Book Printing Ltd; Norfolk, England.

Find Print Reload Images Save Back Forward

All crew members are entitled to append this log. Please state name before inputting then input voice or pen-based data in the usual way.

Space Corps Directive 7713 states:
that the log must be kept up to date at all times with current service records, complete mission data and a comprehensive and accurate list of all crew birthdays so that senior officers may avoid bitter and embarrassing silences when meeting in the corridor with subordinates who have not received a card.

1 Monday

\<Kryten\>
Stupendous start to the new year. Tested new
detergent with built-in stain digesters on 2
pairs of Mr Lister's underpants. It ate them.

2 Tuesday

\<Lister\>
BAD HANGOVER.
Still recovering
from New Year's Eve.

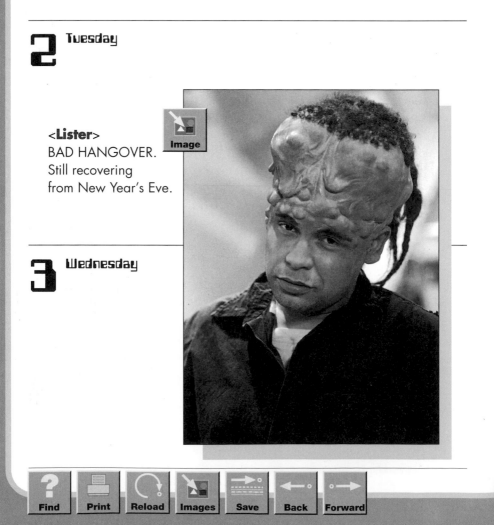

Image

3 Wednesday

Thursday **4**

SPACE CORPS
DIRECTIVE NO 196156
Any officer caught sniffing
the saddle of the exercise
bicycle in the women's
gym will be discharged
without trial.

Friday **5**

<Rimmer, Arnold J>

So busy working out my new year's resolutions missed the first five days of the new year. Must remember to court-martial Holly.

Resolutions:

1. Test sexual applications of hard light holographic form.
2. Eliminate all forms of music throughout galaxy except for Hammond Organ
3. Begin work on long-awaited autobiography – *Arnold Rimmer: Lust for Glory*

Saturday **6**

<Kryten>

Demonstrated to Mr Rimmer how to create new characters in the Artificial Reality games by scanning the ship's historical database. He seemed highly amused by the demonstration.

Sunday **7**

8 Monday

<Lister>
Great! Now Rimmer's overloaded the AR preferences chip battery by having 472 marathon bonks with Catherine the Great.

---

9 Tuesday

<Cat>
With my highly developed feline sense of supersmell, I can sniff out trouble a mile off. Or locate one of Lister's socks in the next galaxy...

10 We

Thursday **11**

<Holly>

Mission Update – as ever, the crew are managing to
work together like a single, well-oiled machine.
Unfortunately the machine's a K-Tel Nose Hair Trimmer.

Friday **12**

<Rimmer, Arnold J>

Post pod arrived containing vids of the complete
works of Sorbik Bjorksson   22nd Century
Sweden's greatest film director. In an effort to raise
flagging morale, have programmed a season of
these classic movies beginning with *The Dichotomy
of Faith in a Post-Materialistic Society* – Sjorbik's
only musical.

Saturday **13**

Sunday **14**

Monday

> **<Lister>**
> Last night's film was DEPRESSING, man. I should've
> suspected something when I saw the vid box and
> instead of a certificate, it had the number of the
> Samaritans.

 **Tuesday**

Wednesday

> **<Kryten>**
> I agree Sunday's film lacked *joie de vivre*.
> However I did feel it came alive during that
> big production number set in the boil clinic – I
> Could Have Lanced All Night. (Joke mode!)

Thursday **18**

\<Rimmer, Arnold J\>
Philistines!

Friday **19**

\<Cat\>
Hey – Rimmer says this book is for posterity, to be read
by future generations, in which case I'd like to share the
greatest bit of Cat wisdom of all. Here it is: "In a boil
wash, never put whites in with colours".

Sunday **21**

22 Monday

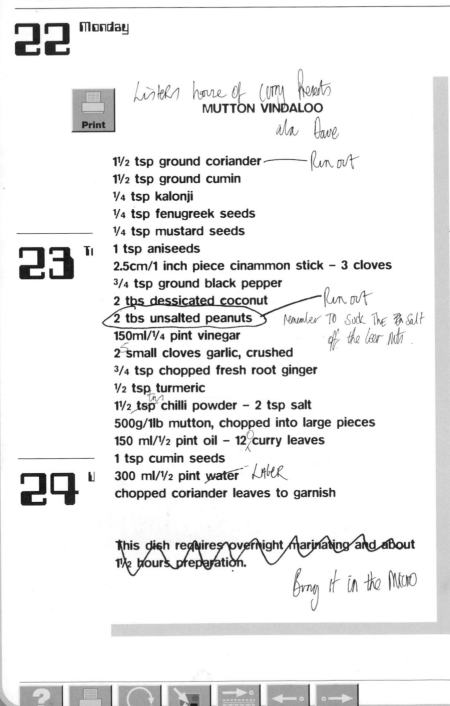

Print

Listers house of curry flavours

MUTTON VINDALOO

ala Dave

1½ tsp ground coriander ——— *Run out*
1½ tsp ground cumin
¼ tsp kalonji
¼ tsp fenugreek seeds
¼ tsp mustard seeds

23 Tu

1 tsp aniseeds
2.5cm/1 inch piece cinammon stick – 3 cloves
¾ tsp ground black pepper
2 tbs dessicated coconut ——— *Run out*
2 tbs unsalted peanuts *Remember to suck the the salt off the beer nuts.*
150ml/¼ pint vinegar
2 small cloves garlic, crushed
¾ tsp chopped fresh root ginger
½ tsp turmeric
1½ tsp chilli powder – 2 tsp salt
500g/1lb mutton, chopped into large pieces
150 ml/½ pint oil – 12 curry leaves
1 tsp cumin seeds

24 W

300 ml/½ pint water *LAGER*
chopped coriander leaves to garnish

This dish requires overnight marinating and about
1½ hours preparation.

Bung it in the Micro

Thursday **25**

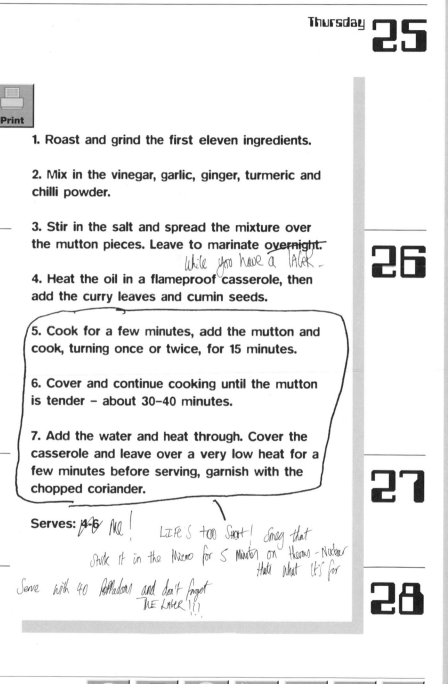

Print

1. Roast and grind the first eleven ingredients.

2. Mix in the vinegar, garlic, ginger, turmeric and chilli powder.

3. Stir in the salt and spread the mixture over the mutton pieces. Leave to marinate overnight.

while you have a TAGER -

4. Heat the oil in a flameproof casserole, then add the curry leaves and cumin seeds.

5. Cook for a few minutes, add the mutton and cook, turning once or twice, for 15 minutes.

6. Cover and continue cooking until the mutton is tender – about 30–40 minutes.

7. Add the water and heat through. Cover the casserole and leave over a very low heat for a few minutes before serving, garnish with the chopped coriander.

Serves: ~~4-6~~ *Me !*

LIFE'S too Short! Sneg that stick it in the Micro for 5 Minutes on Therms - Nuclear thats what It's for

Serve with 40 Poppadoms and don't forget THE LAGER !!!

26

27

28

29 Monday

<Rimmer, Arnold J>
Plan for the remodelling of the interior of the ship
'Red Dwarf' by Arnold J. Rimmer BSc, SSC:

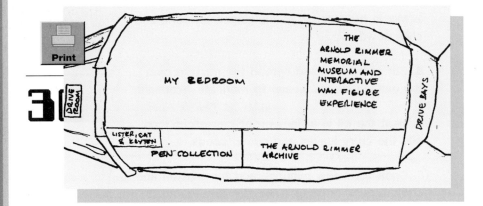

31 Wednesday

<Holly>
Supply status update: we have 14.7 tons of sliced
dill pickle, 9,478 sesame seed baps. And one
hamburger.

Thursday 1

Friday 2

<Holly>
System malfunction! One of the Skutters has
gone berserk and broken into ship's
hardware pod.

<Rimmer, Arnold J>
So? How much harm can it do with a
paintbrush and a jumbo box of Solvite?

Saturday 3

<Lister>
Found rogue Skutter in what was my quarters but is now
a Regency-striped drawing room with Austrian blinds
and wall-hanging fabrics. May have to move; can't
possibly sleep in same cabin as a dado rail.

Sunday 4

5 Monday

\<Lister\>
Me and Kryten redecorated my quarters with a
bucket of chicken jalfrezi, a brush and a paint
roller. Have decided to stay.

6 Tuesday

\<Holly\>
Scans reveal that our water supplies are so low, we
may have to start drinking the Dutch lager.

7 Wednesday   Hammond Organ invented

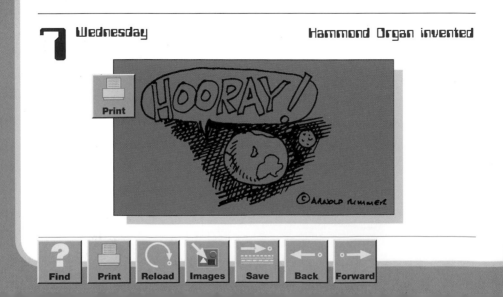

Thursday

<Rimmer, Arnold J>
Valentine's day approaching. Time to take
Rachel out of mothballs, methinks...

<Rimmer, Arnold J>

Friday

Have made Rachel a card. Features me looking
heroic on the front. And inside, a romantic
verse, written in the style of Byron and Shelley
> *I love you 'cause you're not a git,*
> *You love me for my puncture kit.*

12 Monday

<Cat>
Today I'm going to see if I can't
have sex with something.

13 Tuesday

14 Wednesday

<Kryten>

I E5A908B7 You

Thursday **15**

Friday **16**

<**Holly**>
Morale hasn't been this low since Rimmer
accidentally taped three episodes of *World
Championship Risk* over the top of *Beyond The Valley
of the Cheerleaders XXVII: This Time It's Personal.*

Saturday **17**

Sunday **18**

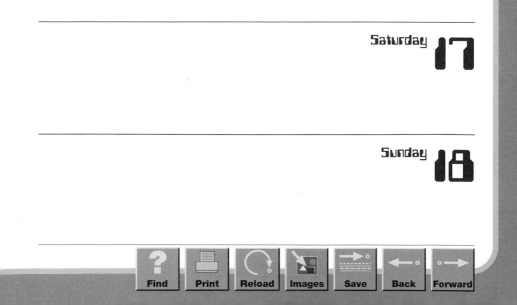

Monday

> **<Lister>**
> Bored. I wonder if you can power an
> Artificial Reality machine by using
> vindaloo sauce.

 **Tuesday**

> **<Lister>**
> Nope.

 Wednesday

SPACE CORPS
DIRECTIVE NO 34124
No officer with false teeth
should attempt oral sex in
zero gravity.

Thursday **22**

Friday **23**

\<Rimmer, Arnold J\>

This week's film in our Sjorbik Bjornsson season
will be his light-hearted action thriller *Beverly Hills
Bereavement Counsellor.*

Attendance is compulsory.

Saturday **24**

\<Cat\>

Sunday **25**

Lister got mad when he found out I was keeping
the last of his basmati rice in my wardrobe. But
hey – I was only doing what it said on the packet:
'Store in a dry, cool place'!

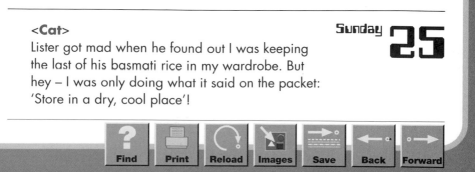

26 Monday

27 Tuesday

<Lister>

Dreamed about Kochanski last night. She was modelling for me while I did this huge, amazing oil painting of her...it looked like this...

28

I don't think I've got the ears quite right.

Thursday 29

<Holly>
Supply status update: food...0.2% of capacity;
water...0.165% of capacity; air supplies...danger
levels. Still, look on the bright side – we do still
have 1,167 spare toilet roll covers in the shape of
little flamenco dancers.

Friday 1

<Rimmer, Arnold J>
re: autobiography, chapter entitled 'My
Favourite Chat-Up Lines':

"Please have sex with me, I'm dead."

<Rimmer, Arnold J>
The anniversary of the saddest day in the history of the
human race.

Saturday 2

<Cat>
You mean this is the day they invented crimpolene?

<Rimmer, Arnold J>
I died, winklepicker teeth.

Sunday 3

4 Monday

Warwick Bedford © BBC 1988

5 Tuesday

6 Wednesd

<Lister>
Love Song (dedicated to Navigation Officer Kristine Kochanski)

Kochanski, Kochanski,
D'you fancy
A danceski?

© Dave Lister 3,000 – and something.

FULL NAME: David Lister

SPECIES: Human

Image

OCCUPATION: Third Technician on the Jupiter Mining Corporation ship Red Dwarf

FORMER OCCUPATION: Trolley Attendant at Sainsbury's Megamarket, Liverpool, Earth

ORIGINS: Found abandoned in a cardboard box under a pool table in a pub. Adopted but father died: told that his father had gone to the same place as his goldfish. Later taken to a child psychologist when found with his head down the bowl reading him the football results.

EDUCATION: Minimal

FURTHER EDUCATION: Failed all exams. 97 minutes at Art College.

SKILLS: Believes himself to be 'Ace pool player' and 'great guitar player'. Has written 'The Indling Song' and the definitive 'Om'.

HOBBIES: ▶ Slobbing ▶ Eating ▶ Zero Gee Football (favourite team London Jets) ▶ Baiting Rimmer ▶ Durex Volleyball

MUSICAL TASTES: Rasta Billy Skank (contains the warning 'May cause disorders of the nervous system and bowels'). First song learnt to play on guitar: 'She's Out Of My Life'.

HEROES: Jim Bexley Speed, the Roof Attack player with the London Jets. Also has a high regard for Ace Rimmer.

ALTER EGOS: Sebastian Doyle, Brett Riverboat, detective Philip in the game 'Gumshoe' and Spanners in Ace's reality.

AMBITIONS: Get back to Earth, marry Kristine Kochanski and buy a farm on Fiji where they will breed horses, cows and sheep. Also has hopes of opening a chain of Hot Dog and Doughnut Diners.

11 Monday

<Rimmer, Arnold J>
The Rimmer Salute – by A. J. Rimmer BSc, SSC

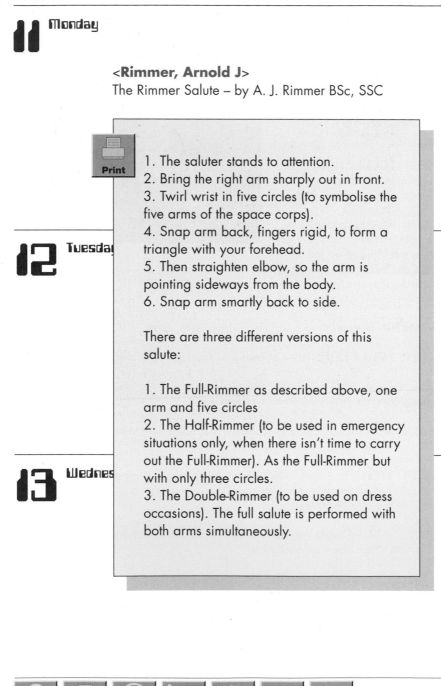

Print

1. The saluter stands to attention.
2. Bring the right arm sharply out in front.
3. Twirl wrist in five circles (to symbolise the five arms of the space corps).
4. Snap arm back, fingers rigid, to form a triangle with your forehead.
5. Then straighten elbow, so the arm is pointing sideways from the body.
6. Snap arm smartly back to side.

There are three different versions of this salute:

1. The Full-Rimmer as described above, one arm and five circles
2. The Half-Rimmer (to be used in emergency situations only, when there isn't time to carry out the Full-Rimmer). As the Full-Rimmer but with only three circles.
3. The Double-Rimmer (to be used on dress occasions). The full salute is performed with both arms simultaneously.

12 Tuesday

13 Wednes

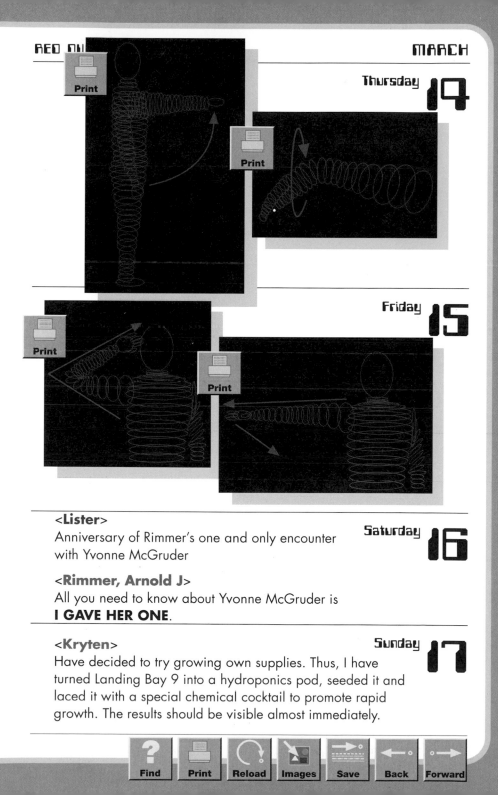

Saturday 16

\<Lister\>
Anniversary of Rimmer's one and only encounter with Yvonne McGruder

\<Rimmer, Arnold J\>
All you need to know about Yvonne McGruder is **I GAVE HER ONE**.

Sunday 17

\<Kryten\>
Have decided to try growing own supplies. Thus, I have turned Landing Bay 9 into a hydroponics pod, seeded it and laced it with a special chemical cocktail to promote rapid growth. The results should be visible almost immediately.

18 Monday

\<Kryten\>
Ship taken over by a 9,000lb greenfly.

19 Tuesday

\<Kryten\>
War with greenfly. Mr Lister asked me to do him a favour,
so I offered to throw myself onto the greenfly, overloading
my power-core and destroying the insect and myself in a
massive neutron blast. Mr Lister said he was thinking more
of me getting him a lager milkshake.

20 Wednesday

\<Cat\>
Lister asked for my help to fight the greenfly. I firmly but
graciously refused on the grounds that I never kill
anything that clashes with my eyes.

Thursday 21

\<Holly\>
ALERT! ALERT!!! We are down to our last two cans
of pineapple chunks.
Oh, by the way – there's a meteorite the size of
Woking but with better architecture on a collision
course with us...

\<Cat\>
This sounds like a 12 change of underwear trip!

Birth of Andrew Lloyd Webber

Friday 22

\<Rimmer, Arnold J\>
Came up with brilliant plan to commandeer
Starbug and hightail it off the ship before meteor
hit. But before I could steal the ignition key from
Lister, Kryten opened the rear bay doors,
propelling the greenfly into space where it smashed
into the meteorite and deflected it from its course.
Incredible coincidence, as that was my backup plan.

Saturday 23

Sunday 24

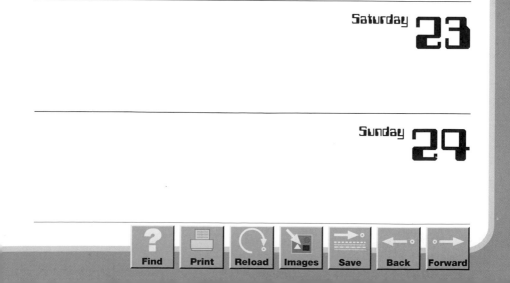

25 Monday

\<Kryten>

Mr Lister, I have decided to try and acquire the human skill of 'drawing' so to this end, I have taken the liberty of drawing a picture of you:

26 Tuesday

\<Kryten>

Do you think I've made your hair too long?

27 Wednesday

\<Rimmer, Arnold J>

From my cuttings file:

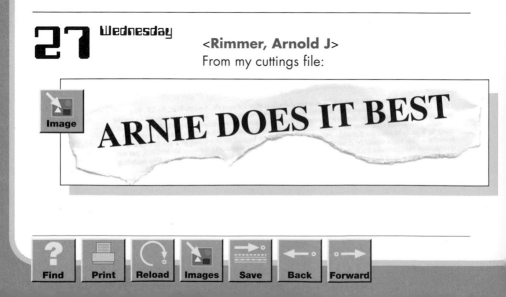

ARNIE DOES IT BEST

<Lister>
Me this time last year.

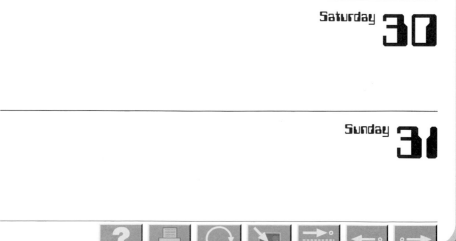

Saturday **30**

Sunday **31**

1 Monday

<Holly>
Have made contact with Earth. It is now being run by a species descended from Car Park Attendants. I can land but we can't afford to stay longer than an hour.

2 Tuesday

<Holly>
APRIL, MAY, JUNE, JULY AND AUGUST FOOL!!!!

3 Wednesday

<Lister>
We know. It was funny the first time, Holly.

<Rimmer, Arnold J>
But after 6 years, frankly, you need some new material.

Thursday 4

Friday 5

<Kryten>
I have an excellent joke for you, Holly. Why did the
electron cross the biosphere?

Saturday 6

<Holly>
Because no one has yet repealed the 8th Law of Kinetics.

Sunday 7

<Kryten>
Oh, you've heard it.

8 Monday

<Lister>
Guitar practice.

9 Tuesday

10 Wednesday

To Ganymede and Titan,
Yes sir, I've been around,
But there ain't no place
in the whole of space,
Like the good ol' toddlin' town.....

Lunar City Seven,
You're my idea of heaven.
Out of ten, you score eleven,
You good ol' artificial terra-formed
settlement...

Thursday 11

Friday 12

Saturday 13

<Lister>
Supplies low. AR machine still broken. Bored.
Hungry. Only music and memories of mutton
vindaloo keeping me going. Last night I had a
dream where I curried my guitar.

Sunday 14

15 Monday

<Kryten>
Oh, for a really world-class psychiatrist!

16 Tuesday

17

Print

Rear Admiral Lieutenant General Rimmer
Red Dwarf
Deep Space
RE1 3DW

Dear Rimmer,

I hope this epistle finds you adequately healthy
to discharge your duties. I write to inform you
that your father is dead. He passed away peacefully
in his jeep.

Mother.

Thursday
18

Friday **19**

\<Kryten\>
Supply levels in the Red Zone. However, did
discover tin of dog food which I casseroled for
Mr Lister's supper...

Saturday
20

\<Lister\>
Well, now I can see why dogs lick their testicles.
It's to take away the taste of the food.

Sunday **21**

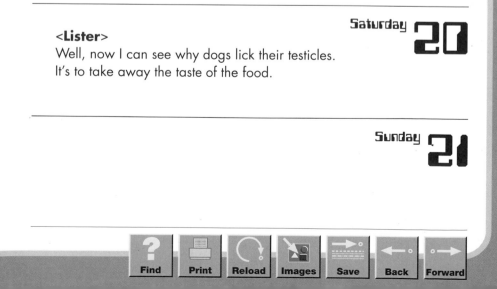

22 Monday

---

23 Tuesday

<Holly>
Dave, I'm not saying our food supplies are getting low...but if I were you I'd stop biting your nails for a couple of weeks or you'll have nothing to eat when you get REALLY hungry.

---

24 Wednesday

<Cat>
Great day! Had a manicure...a pedicure...a facial...then chased a space weevil across 16 decks. I love a run before dinner!

Thursday 25

\<Kryten\>
Have taken drastic measures to curb the Red
Dwarf food shortage:

Space Weevil au Mechanoid

Simply take ...
1. 1 space weevil (per person)
2. Marinate in wine re-cyc.
   overnight.
3. Drain thoroughly.
4. Lightly grill under a moderate
   heat, turning occasionally, until
   golden brown.
5. Serve with fresh vegetables to
   distract Mr Lister.
6. Pray that it tastes like Crunchy
   King Prawn...

Print

Friday 26

Image

Saturday 27

Sunday 28

 Monday

---

30 Tuesday

SPACE CORPS
DIRECTIVE NO 997
Work done by an officer's
doppelganger in a parallel
universe cannot be
claimed as overtime.

---

1 Wednesday

<Lister>
Me and Kryten got erased from history.

<Kryten>
All in all, today's been a bit of a bummer,
hasn't it sir?

Thursday 2

<Rimmer, Arnold J>
3am. Nightwatch. My thoughts turn to death...on which
I'm a bit of an expert. I knew one chap on Red Dwarf,
who was totally obsessed with it. He'd read most people
die in their sleep...about 3am – so he decided never to
be asleep at 3. Set alarm bells, klaxons, sirens in his
quarters, all to go off every morning at 2.59. Ironic
really. Within a week, he was dead. And he died at
3am. The bloke in the bunk below shot him.

Friday 3

Saturday 4

<Holly>
Today we came across a moon which was shaped
exactly like Felicity Kendal's bottom.
We flew around that one a couple of times.

Sunday 5

6 Monday

7 Tuesday

8 Wednesday

<Rimmer, Arnold J>
The man who sweats madras sauce.

Thursday
9

Friday 10

<Lister>
ZERO-G LOVE SONG

When it's done in Zero-G
Sex is fun for you and me
But what can be a tragedy
Is visiting the lavatory

© Dave Lister 3,000 and a bit.

Saturday 11

<Cat>
AAAAAAAARGHHHHHHHHHHHHHH!!!!
Bad hair day!!!!

Sunday 12

13 Monday

\<Kryten\>
Reviewing visual data record 1267/K: Camille
Love means never having to say you're a
mono-optic mucoid meta-mutant.

14 Tuesday

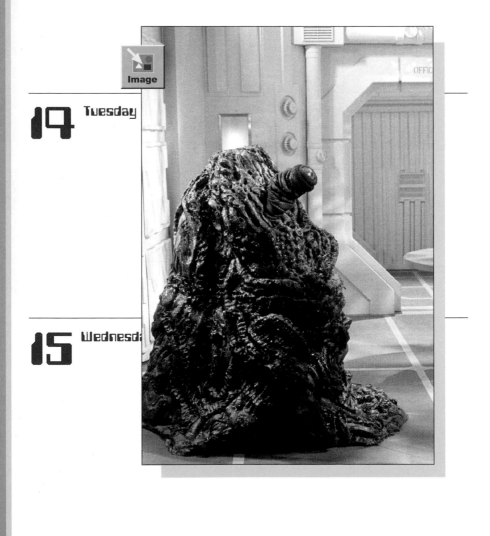

15 Wednesday

Thursday 16

<Cat>
I've got a beautiful ASS.

Friday 17

<Rimmer, Arnold J>
After the mass walkout during last week's
Sjorbik Bkjorksson film, have decided to
programme his most blatantly commercial
film for tonight – the romantic comedy *Four
Funerals and Another One*.

Saturday 18

Sunday 19

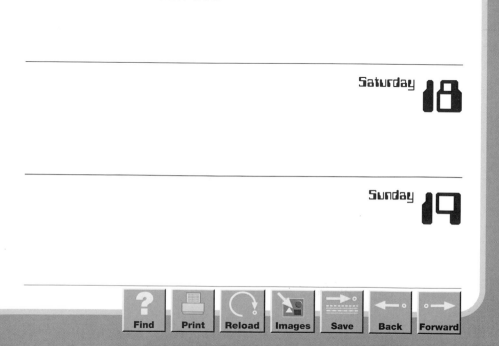

20 Monday

21 Tuesday

22 Wednesday

<Lister>
Haircut. Cat usually does it but he'd just started
styling his own hair and I didn't want to wait till
Thursday. Got skutters to do it instead – looks
pretty good!

<Lister>
Me after my mow and blow.

Friday 24

Saturday 25

<Kryten>
Spin my nipple nuts and send me to Alaska! Today
I found 10 episodes of *Androids* on video tape.
Almost as much fun as scrubbing Mr. Lister's gussets.

Sunday 26

27 Monday

<Rimmer, Arnold J>
notes for autobiography – **BEING DEAD**

Advantages
1. Whenever anyone asks 'how are you?' can wittily reply 'I'm DEAD, actually!'
2. Life Insurance salesmen no longer a problem.
3. Impresses the women.

Disadvantages
1. No longer possible to sing first line of the song 'Fame' with any degree of conviction whatsoever.

28 Tuesday

<Kryten>
Visual memory data review 3479/U: The Inquisitor

'Justify Yourself'

29 Wednesday

Thursday **30**

Friday **31**

<Rimmer, Arnold J>
All right – who put my Sjorbik Bjorksson vids in the
garbage vaporizer?

<Holly>
Everyone did, Arnold...

Saturday **1**

<Holly>
Have now been travelling through deep space for
approximately 3,000,207 years, 45 days, 7 hours
and three minutes. And have we passed one bloody
'Happy Eater'?

Sunday **2**

3 Monday

4 Tue

5 Wed

STAR CORPS PERSONNEL MANUAL

3.2
EXPLORING A POTENTIALLY HOSTILE WORLD

DO'S & DON'TS

UPON LANDING:

DO – avoid all eye contact.

DON'T – use the phrase 'Greetings, mutants, we have come to conquer your planet', even in fun.

UPON MEETING GELF TRIBAL LEADERS:

DO – praise tentacles (where applicable).

DON'T – say 'phoarr! Where's that funny stink coming from, slime-lobes?'

DO – emphasise the mutual benefits that a meeting of two great socio-cultural systems could produce.

DON'T – vomit.

This is the toughie

Print

Thursday 6

<Rimmer, Arnold J>
Found this picture of Lister's wife. Proving the
theory that men do tend to marry women who
look like them.

<Lister>
Smeg off, Rimmer!

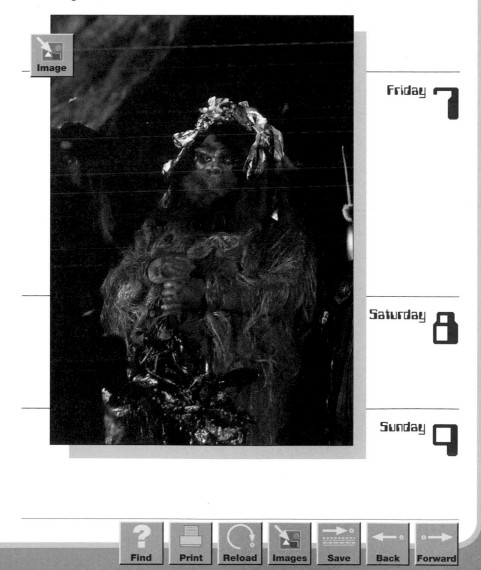

Friday 7

Saturday 8

Sunday 9

17 Monday

FULL NAME: Arnold Judas Rimmer.

SPECIES: Of human origin; hologram since radiation leak. Now has a light bee that can give him limited hard-light status, allowing him to touch things.

OCCUPATION: Second Technician with the Jupiter Mining Corporation in charge of Z Shift aboard Red Dwarf.

FORMER OCCUPATION: None.

ORIGINS: Born on Io, one of Jupiter's moons. Refers to mother as a 'bitch queen from Hell'; father used to put Rimmer and his brothers on a rack to make them tall enough to enter the Space Corps Academy.

EDUCATION: Sent to Io House (unlike his brothers. Blames his not becoming an officer on this fact.) Also attended Cadet School.

FURTHER EDUCATION: Maintenance course at Saturn Tech. Has been trying for years to learn Esperanto.

SKILLS: Disciplined, organised, dedicated to his career. Always has a pen.

HOBBIES: ▶ Morris dancing ▶ Holidaying in the diesel decks ▶ Owns a collection of photographs of Twentieth Century Telegraph Poles ▶ Playing Risk (has kept a record of every game played since Cadet School) ▶ Leads the skutters in Hammond Organ Recital Night. (See MUSICAL TASTES.)

MUSICAL TASTES: Reggie Wilson, (whose style of Hammond Organ music has produced 'Reggie Wilson Plays the Lift Music Classics' and 'Funking up Wagner'. Reggie Dixon's 'Tango Treats' and several James Last albums.

HEROES: Napoleon Bonaparte General George S. Patton, whose sinal fluid he owns.

ALTER EGOS: William Doyle (half brother of Sebastian), Ace Rimmer (What a guy), Dangerous Dan McGrew

AMBITIONS: To get a body, get back to Earth, and find a woman who doesn't want to vomit over him in disgust. His most burning ambition is to become an officer.

Thursday **13**

    \<Lister\>
Bored.

Friday **14**

    \<Lister\>
Found parallel universe.

Saturday **15**

    \<Lister\>
Saved parallel universe from certain destruction.

Sunday **16**

    \<Lister\>
Came home.

17 Monday

> **\<Lister\>**
> Bored again.

18 Tu

19 Wed

> **\<Cat\>**
> Sexual magnetism is a virus? Well, get
> me to a hospital – I'm a terminal case!

Friday 2l

‹Rimmer, Arnold J›

In view of the exceptional bravery he exhibited
whilst in the parallel universe – bravery that went
far beyond the call of duty – I have no hesitation
in recommending Second Technician Arnold J.
Rimmer (heretoforeinafter referred to as 'me') for
an immediate promotion, pay increase and a
company shuttle (red, with a Blautechpunknicht
stereo and really crappy fuel consumption).

Saturday 22

Sunday 23

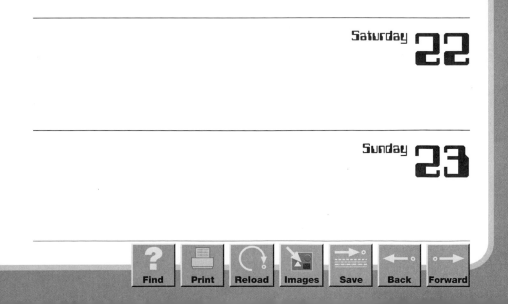

24 Monday

\<Kryten\>

Have discovered a way to convert the small, hard balls of rolled up tissue found in Mr Lister's pockets on laundry day into a new form of propulsive fuel. Each ball provides enough power for a day's flying – so we shouldn't have to worry about refuelling for at least the next 978 years.

25 Tuesday

26 Wednesday

\<Lister\>

Love Song

© Dave Lister 3,000 and something

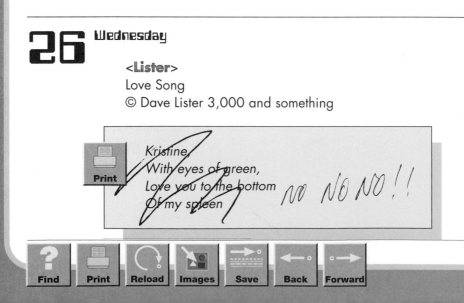

Kristine,
With eyes of green,
Love you to the bottom
Of my spleen

NO NO NO !!

Print

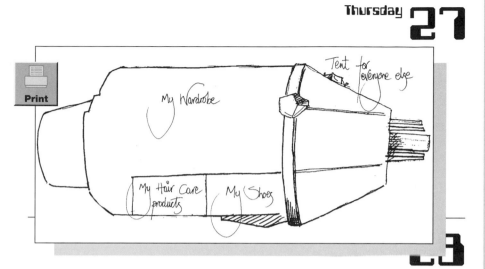

My Wardrobe

Tent for everyone else

My Hair Care products

My Shoes

<Cat>
How about we renovate the ship like this?

Saturday **29**

Sunday **30**

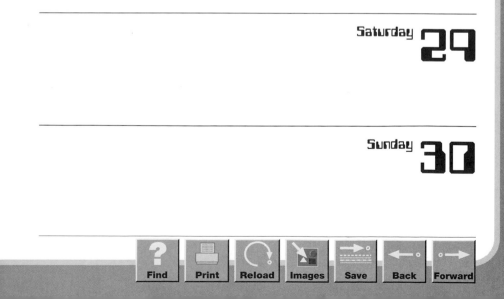

1 Monday

<Lister>
Kryten fixed the Artificial Reality machine with a battery from the parallel universe – so tomorrow we're off on our hols into the 'Holiday In Europe' program we found on derelict.

2 Tuesday

SPACE CORPS
DIRECTIVE NO 7214
To preserve morale during long-haul missions, all male officers above the rank of First Technician must, during panto season, be ready to put on a dress and a pair of false breasts.

3 Wednesday

<Rimmer, Arnold J>
Spent day under heavy artillery bombardment from Axis Forces – on account of smeghead Lister getting the 'Holiday in Europe' program mixed up with the smegging 'Victory In Europe' one!!!

<Lister>
Stop whingeing, Rimmer. At least it makes a change.

Thursday 4

<Rimmer, Arnold J>
A change?!? Lister, I'm on holiday. I want peace.
Quiet. Margaritas by the pool. Topless beach
babes to ogle. Which is why 'Occupied France'
has never been at the top of my holiday
destination list!!! Cancel the program!

Friday 5

<Kryten>
Unfortunately, the 'cancel' option on this program
has been disabled. We will just have to proceed
overland to Berlin, dodge the occupation forces,
and assassinate Adolf Hitler.

Saturday 6

Sunday 7

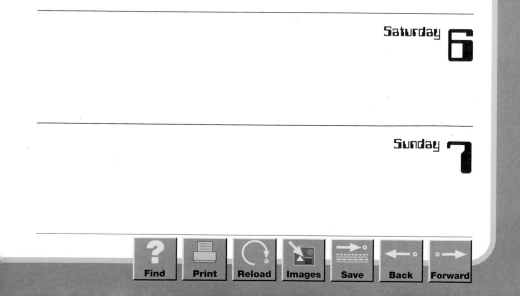

8 Monday

<Rimmer, Arnold J>
Oh great. Fine!!! We're about to go up
against the massed forces of the Third
Reich armed with a Bugs Bunny beach
blanket and a bottle of Ambre Solaire.

9 Tuesday

<Lister>
Yeh. But look on the bright side – it's Factor
38 Ambre Solaire.

10 Wed

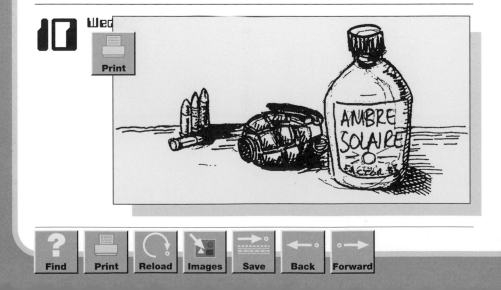

Thursday 11

<Lister>
Joined Resistance.

Friday 12

<Cat>
Hey, these Resistance babes are CUTE! But no
way am I putting on that stupid green and brown
jacket – you won't be able to see me against the
landscape!!!

Saturday 13

<Kryten>
Began march on Berlin.

Sunday 14

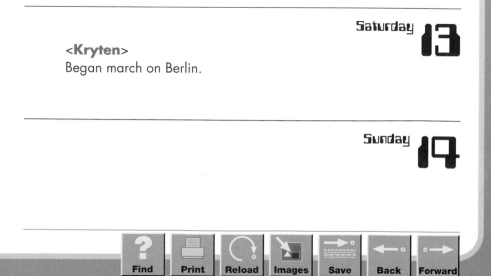

15 Monday

<Lister>
Took Bridge at Remagen. Rimmer ran up to
German platoon shouting "I'm a Nazi – honest!!!"

<Rimmer, Arnold J>
I was just trying to distract them!

16 Tuesday

17 Wednesday

<Kryten>
We are now in Berlin, where I have offered to
sacrifice myself by turning my head into a small
thermonuclear device and detonating it in the
foyer of Third Reich Headquarters. Mr Rimmer
told me to go ahead, but Mr Lister not so keen.

Thursday **18**

Friday **19**

\<Lister\>

We're back on Red Dwarf after discovering the game had an unexpected 'cheat' built into it. Hitler died of a broken heart when Cat eloped with Eva Braun.

\<Cat\>

The chick was hot!!!

\<Rimmer, Arnold J\>

Saturday **20**

Lister, that is positively the LAST time I ever go on holiday with you till half past hell-freezes-over. It was the most horrendous time I've had since they closed down 'Club 18-30'. Appalling food, prehistoric accomodation – and wherever we went we were shot at by Nazis!

Sunday **21**

\<Lister\>

Typical British tourist. Go abroad and do nothing but complain about the Germans.

22 Monday

23

\<Rimmer, Arnold J\>
Say what you like – next year I'm going to have a PROPER holiday. Rambling on the Diesel Deck…

24 Wednesday

Thursday 25

<Rimmer, Arnold J>

Decided to study Esperanto. I will single
mindedly dedicate myself to becoming fluent
in this wonderful, universal, language.
Nothing will stand in my way. Nothing.

Friday 26

<Rimmer, Arnold J>

Ignore everything I said yesterday about
Esperanto – decided to watch a documentary
about 'Being Single Minded'. Well I watched
half of it and then got bored and did
something else instead.

> **SPACE CORPS
> DIRECTIVE NO 723**
> Terraformers are expressly
> forbidden from recreating
> Swindon.

Saturday 27

Sunday 28

<Lister>

Played Durex Volleyball with Cat.

29 Monday

---

30 Tuesday

<Kryten>

My artistic prowess is growing with practice!
Today I managed to produce a very faithful
reproduction of Da Vinci's 'La Giaconda'.

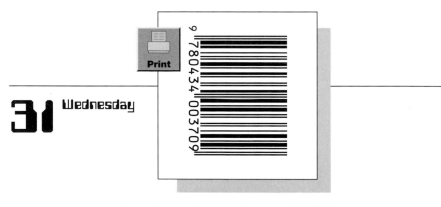

31 Wednesday

Apart from the smile, it's indistinguishable from
the original!

thursday 1

Find

FULL NAME: Cat

SPECIES: Felis Sapiens

Image

OCCUPATION: Does not do the 'W' word

FORMER OCCUPATION: None.

ORIGINS: Lister's cat Frankenstein. Evolved in cargo hold over 3 million years. Parents thought to be a cripple and an idiot, as they were the only cats left aboard after the Cat Wars

2

EDUCATION: Instructed in the Seven Cat Commandments. Learnt of the Holy Mother, Frankenstein, and the true father of Catkind, Cloister (or Clister) the Stupid who would return to lead them to the Promised Land of Fuchal. Was also taught how to read cat-style by sniffing the blank pages of cat books.

FURTHER EDUCATION: Rimmer taught him to operate the vending machines on Red Dwarf as a bribe to hand over Lister's cigarettes. Can also pilot Starbug.

SKILLS: Looking good, eating and sleeping. He has recently developed his nasal abilities to a very high standard.

HOBBIES: ► Looking good ► Eating ► Sleeping ► Games: very partial to a game of Junior Angler Soap Sud Slalom and Unicycle Polo Playing with his shiny yo-yo

3

MUSICAL TASTES: 'Tongue tied' (once dreamt that he was singing it accompanied by the rest of the crew on backing vocals). A twisted tape of 'Robert Hardy reads "Tess of the D'urbervilles"

ALTER EGOS: Duane Dibbley, The Riviera Kid and a Priest

4

AMBITIONS: To have sex with anything that smells better than Lister.

5 Monday

<Rimmer, Arnold J>

In the tragic absence of anything resembling a woman in the universe, have inaugurated the annual Red Dwarf 'Erotic Fiction' competition. First trouser-tightening effort below...

The moment she saw the gorgeous hologram with the ~~xxxxxxxxxx~~ *she knew her* ~~xxxxxx~~ *would never* ~~xxxxxxxx~~ *Preparing the diamante jockstrap for a* ~~xxxxxxxx~~ *rubber wimple, but without it* ~~xxxxxxxx~~ ~~xxxxx~~ *fondant nipple icing.* ~~xxxxxxxx~~ *underpants* ~~xxxxxxx~~ *cucumber relish.*

6 Tuesday

<Lister>

Rimmer – I've seen more erotic knitting patterns!

<Kryten>

Mr Rimmer, I have taken the liberty of crossing out all misspelt words in your story so your literary reputation will not suffer in the future. Also, I have an entry for your competition...

7 Wedn

EROTIC MODE (FICTION):
"CIRCUIT-BOARDS OF PASSION"
(not to be viewed by life forms under the age of 18)

Fasten wing nut over flange bracket below pump module. Press button 'C' to disengage ionic baseplate unit, rethreading indicator array and aligning....

Excuse me!!! I feel a SUDDEN, URGENT NEED for a liquid nitrogen shower!!!

<Lister>
Marathon curry night!!!
Drank a yard of vindaloo sauce.

Saturday 10

<Lister>
Spent day on toilet deck.

Sunday 11

<Lister>
Ditto.

Find   Print   Reload   Images   Save   Back   Forward

12 Monday

<Rimmer, Arnold J>
Notes for autobiography, chapter entitled
'My Brilliant Career':
My first attempt at the First Technician's exam
revealed a restless, enquiring mind, but also
several small gaps in my grasp of fine detail...

13 Tue

14 We

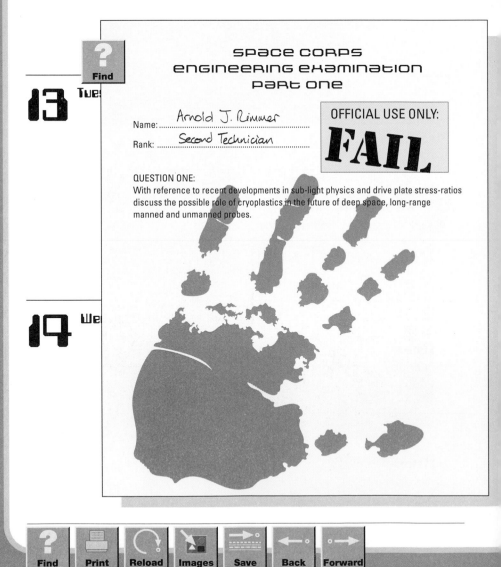

space corps engineering examination part one

Name: Arnold J. Rimmer

Rank: Second Technician

OFFICIAL USE ONLY:

FAIL

QUESTION ONE:
With reference to recent developments in sub-light physics and drive plate stress-ratios
discuss the possible role of cryoplastics in the future of deep space, long-range
manned and unmanned probes.

\<Kryten\>
Reviewing visual data memory...

It's a small, off-duty Czechoslovakian traffic warden.

Monday

>**<Holly>**
>A Stasis Leak is a leak, right, in stasis,
>hence the name Stasis Leak.

 **Tuesday**

 **Wednesday**

>**<Lister>**
>Quiet day.

Thursday 22

<Lister>
Uneventful day.

Friday 23

<Cat>
Oh LORD!!! RED ALERT!!! SEND OUT A DISTRESS SIGNAL!!! SOUND A GALAXY-WIDE EMERGENCY!!! This is IT!!! THE END OF LIFE AS WE KNOW IT!!

Saturday 24

<Lister>
Cat got a zit.

Sunday 25

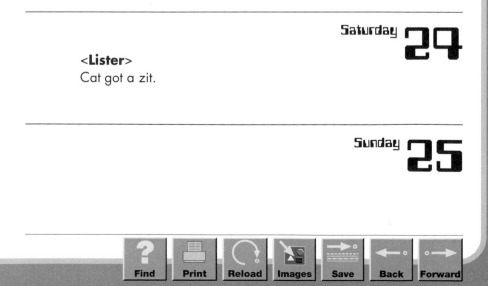

Find   Print   Reload   Images   Save   Back   Forward

26 Monday

<Kryten>
Mr Rimmer has taken to waking us every morning
with a selection of Hammond Organ melodies.
Sadly, Mr Rimmer cannot play the organ, so he is
rendering them on comb and paper.

I believe Mr Lister is becoming suicidal.

27 Tuesday

28

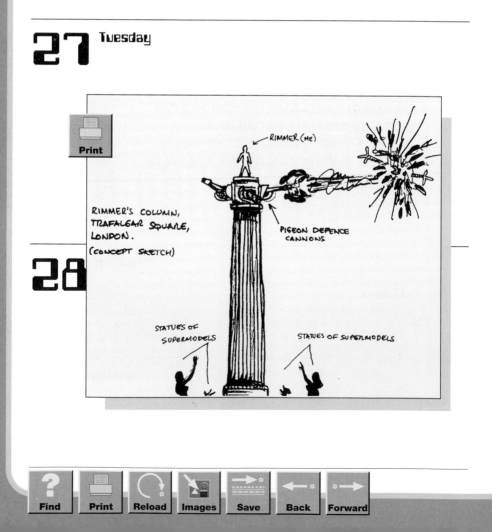

RIMMER (ME)

RIMMER'S COLUMN,
TRAFALGAR SQUARE,
LONDON.
(CONCEPT SKETCH)

PIGEON DEFENCE
CANNONS

STATUES OF
SUPERMODELS

STATUES OF SUPERMODELS

Thursday  29

\<Rimmer, Arnold J>
Date with Rachel.

Friday  30

Saturday  31

Sunday 1

2 Monday

FULL NAME: Holly

SPECIES: Tenth generation AI hologramatic computer.

OCCUPATION: Red Dwarf's mainframe computer.

3 Tu

FORMER OCCUPATION: None.

ORIGINS: Manufactured by the Jupiter Mining Corporation for service on Red Dwarf.

EDUCATION: Has been programmed with an IQ of 6,000

FURTHER EDUCATION: Constantly updates memory banks by referring to the Junior Colour Encyclopaedia of Space.

SKILLS: Perfectly capable of day-to-day running of Red Dwarf despite suspected presence of the computer virus Senility which could reduce IQ quite drastically. Self-confessed blind spot for sevens.

HOBBIES: ▶ Extensive collection of singing potatoes ▶ Reading, in particular Agatha Christie novels.

4 W

MUSICAL TASTES: The Carpenters 'Good-bye to Love'. Dislikes Olivia Newton-John records. Totally revolutionised the music world for Hol Rock by inventing two new notes, Woh and Boh (triangles would have to have four sides and women would be banned from playing the cello).

ALTER EGOS: Melly and Queeg 500.

AMBITIONS: To be restored to former glory and be able to count without banging head on the screen

Thursday 5

<Holly>
Annual self-maintenance month. First – memory management. And there is a way to squeeze 954 gigabytes of memory into 427 gigabytes of disk space. Only I don't remember what it is…

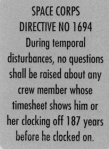

SPACE CORPS
DIRECTIVE NO 1694
During temporal disturbances, no questions shall be raised about any crew member whose timesheet shows him or her clocking off 187 years before he clocked on.

Friday 6

<Kryten>
Watched a classic episode of *Androids* tonight. Kelly told Brook that Brook Jnr was not his android.

Saturday 7

Sunday 8

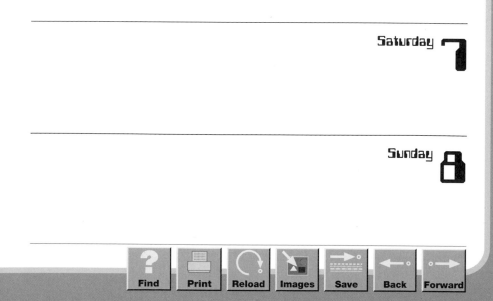

Find　Print　Reload　Images　Save　Back　Forward

9 Monday

10 Tuesday

11 Wednesday

<Holly>
Ooops! Have accidentally overwritten our entire
Rock 'n' Roll sound archive with soundtrack
albums from old Tommy Steele films. Sorry...

\<Lister\>
Am scanning in this great book I found
in parallel universe:

Print

Space Corps Specialist Publications Present:

TERRAFORMING
MADE EASY

101 Handy Hints for the
ultimate Planetary Makeover

Contents

1. Beginner's Terraform

How to transform a barren, desert planet into a world
of verdant pasture, trees and valleys.
How to get rid of giant greenflies.

2. Intermediate Terraform

How to pour a thick layer of tarmac and concrete
over the verdant pastures, trees and meadows.

3. Advanced Terraform

Cutting down the trees, punching a hole in the ozone
layer and adding effluent to the the oceans for that
authentic 'just like home' feel.

 **Monday**

 **Tuesday**

<**Holly**>
Sorry about last night. Amazing how easy it is to get the self-destruct subroutine mixed up with the Hot Chocolate vending sequence…

Wednesday

Image

<Lister>
What a guy!!!

23 Monday

<Rimmer, Arnold J>
Esperanto evening class: Bonvolu alsendi la
pordiston-laûsajne estas rano en mia bideo.

<Kryten>
A frog? In which bidet?

24 Tuesday

25 Wednesday

<Kryten>
Visual memory scan 1232/A: Hudzen

No silicon heaven? Where do all the
calculators go?

Thursday 26

Friday 27

<Holly>
Er...sorry to bother everyone. But I think my
maintenance programme just accidentally ejected the
entire toilet block into space...

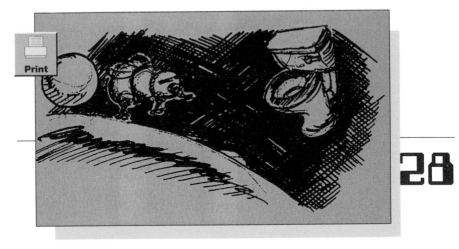

Print

28

Sunday 29

<Rimmer, Arnold J>
Despite a very generous offer from Cat to share his litter
tray on Deck 9, Lister insisted we launch Starbug in
pursuit of the toilet block.

30 Monday

1 Tuesday

<Rimmer, Arnold J>

Operation Khazi a complete success. The skill and daring shown by one man in retrieving those toilets is sure to pass into space legend, which is why I have no hesitation in recommending him for the highest space honours available. His name: Arnold J. Rimmer.

2 Wednesday

SPACE CORPS
DIRECTIVE NO 43872
Suntans will be worn
during off-duty hours only.

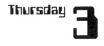

Thursday 3

<**Kryten**>
Mr Lister's Breakfast Menu:

Find

Prawn Bangalore Phall

Half Rice, Half Chips

Seven Spicy Poppadoms

Lager-flavour Milkshake

Two Rennies

Friday 4

Saturday 5

Sunday 6

<**Holly**>
Crew Status – Arnold has spent the last 3 days cross-referencing his collection of Telegraph Pole Slides, Cat's been asleep, Kryten has decided to count all the molecules on the ship – and Dave's offered to help him. Call it a hunch – but I think everyone's bored.

7 Monday

<Rimmer, Arnold J>
Have decided to revive crew morale using regulation morale boosting procedure – waking them every morning at 4am to partake in rousing chorus of Space Corps anthem (all 23 stanzas); compulsory hourly cold showers and compulsory enrolment into my ongoing daily Risk Championship. That should cheer them up!

8 Tuesday

9 Wednesday

<Kryten>
We noticed an alien invasion fleet off the starboard bow. Thankfully it turned out to be one of Mr Lister's old sneezes that had congealed on to the radar screen.

Friday
11

<Rimmer, Arnold J>
After 4 days of my invigorating new daily
regimen, a sense of joyful euphoria pervades
our daily routine. Morale is at an indisputable
all-time high – as any of the crew will tell you.
Right Krytie?

Saturday
12

<Kryten>
I cannot comment on your remark, sir, as I have
been programmed not to lie.

Sunday
13

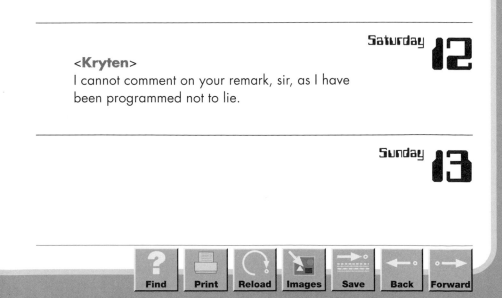

 **Monday**

> **\<Lister\>**
> Cat told me that Rimmer is really getting
> on his tits.
>
> **\<Cat\>**
> Yeah! And coming from someone with six
> nipples, that's a pretty serious complaint!

 **Tuesday**

 **Wednesday**

Thursday **17**

<Rimmer, Arnold J>
It is my duty to be a complete and utter bastard.

ᴅᵃʸ **18**

<Holly>
Purple Alert!
Purple Alert!
It's not as bad as a red
alert, but a bit worse
than a blue alert.

ᵤʳᵈᵃʸ **19**

ᴅᵃʸ **20**

**Monday**

\<Rimmer, Arnold J\>
Holly has detected 2 derelict garbage tankers in our sector. As senior officer, I will naturally be leading the expedition to investigate them – as soon as I check they are uninhabited.

Tuesday

\<Rimmer, Arnold J\>
Holly reckons there ARE life readings on one of those garbage ships. For my part, I feel it's only fair to step aside and give Lister the invaluable command experience he craves. He shall lead the expedition while I remain here to co-ordinate efforts.

\<Lister\>
Rimmer, you....

Wednesday

\<Holly\>
I've recalibrated my sensors and it turns out I was wrong. It's not actually a life form as such. It's a 3-million-year-old Pepperami.

\<Rimmer, Arnold J\>
Have relieved Lister of command of mission due to his unauthorized use of the word 'Smeghead'. I will lead, accompanied by Cat...as soon as he finds his travel hairdryer.

Thursday 24

<Rimmer, Arnold J>
Ran into a spot of trouble on garbage ship,
when we were ambushed by Pepperami as we
boarded. Believe me, it's no fun being attacked
by a 3-million-year-old mutated snack-food. I
bravely fought it off…

<Cat>
Actually, I ate it.

Friday 25

<Rimmer, Arnold J>
…and led the mission to great success. We
manage to scavenge a king's ransom. Well, a
box of Christmas crackers, another toilet roll
holder in the shape of a flamenco dancer and
5 issues of Playgelf which were of such a lewd
and disgusting nature I had to place them
under house arrest under my pillow.

Saturday 26

<Cat>
Reality check, man – the mission was a
DISASTER! 9 million cubic feet of space
between them…and not one goddam tube
of hair-gel!!!

Sunday 27

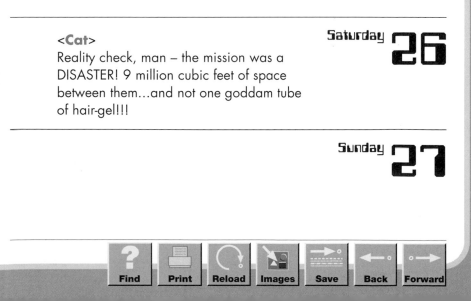

28 Monday

<Kryten>
Reviewing visual memory data 1246/P: Rogue Simulant

Have infection, will travel

29 Tu

30 Wednesday

<Lister>
The Indling Song

Our love I tried to kindle
Like firelight it dwindles
Now I wonder when this wind'll
Ever stop.

© Dave Lister 3,000 and a bit.

Thursday **31**

Find

Image

FULL NAME:
Kryten 2X4B 523P

SPECIES:
Series 4000 Mechanoid

OCCUPATION:
Service android; duties include cooking, cleaning and general dogsbody

FORMER OCCUPATION: Service android Nova 5; duties included cooking, cleaning and general dogsbody

ORIGINS: Manufactured by Diva-Droid International. Overrode built-in obsolescence function to stay with Red Dwarf crew

EDUCATION: Programmed when assembled with a number of skill chips

FURTHER EDUCATION: Has been taught by Lister to rebel and lie by showing him such films as 'Rebel Without A Cause' and 'Casablanca'. As a result is really getting the hang of his 'Lie Mode'.

SKILLS: Has learnt to pilot Starbug and passed the pilot's examination. Speaks fluent Esperanto. Excellent sandwich-maker (uses a set square). Taught to play the piano by Ace Rimmer. Scrubs a mean gusset.

HOBBIES: ▶ Work ▶ Watching *Androids* ▶ Sleeping

MUSICAL TASTES: Enjoys Copacabana (uses this tune when he is off-line).

HEROES: Programmed to respect and obey all humans. Looks up to Lister, who possesses all the qualities he most admires in humans.

ALTER EGOS: Jake Bullet, Sammy the Squib, Bongo. Human for a little while.

AMBITIONS: To find a planet with a suitable atmosphere and grow flowers and trees in his own garden. Failing that he would love to get that really stubborn stain out of Lister's long-johns.

ay **1**

2

3

4 Monday

<Rimmer, Arnold J>
notes for autobiography, chapter entitled
'My Brilliant Career'.

My second attempt at the First Technician's exam –
a bracing experience intellectually, but frustrating to
come so close without quite passing...

? Find

5

SPACE CORPS
ENGINEERING EXAMINATION
PART ONE

Name: _Arnold J. Rimmer_

Rank: _Second Technician_

OFFICIAL USE ONLY:

FAIL

QUESTION ONE:
With reference to recent developments in sub-light physics and drive plate stress-ratios discuss the possible role of cryoplastics in the future of deep space, long-range manned and unmanned probes.

I AM A FISH	I AM A FISH	I AM A FISH	I AM A FISH
I AM A FISH	I AM A FISH	I AM A FISH	I AM A FISH
I AM A FISH	I AM A FISH	I AM A FISH	I AM A FISH
I AM A FISH	I AM A FISH	I AM A FISH	I AM A FISH
I AM A FISH	I AM A FISH	I AM A FISH	I AM A FISH
I AM A FISH	I AM A FISH	I AM A FISH	I AM A FISH
I AM A FISH	I AM A FISH	I AM A FISH	I AM A FISH
I AM A FISH	I AM A FISH	I AM A FISH	I AM A FISH
I AM A FISH	I AM A FISH	I AM A FISH	I AM A FISH
I AM A FISH	I AM A FISH	I AM A FISH	I AM A FISH

6

Thursday 7

<Holly>
Anniversary of Dr Haydn Bassoon's discovery of
what the appendix is really for (medium wave
reception).

Friday 8

SPACE CORPS
DIRECTIVE NO 147
Crew members are
expressly forbidden from
leaving their vessel except
on production of a permit.
Permits can only be issued
by the Chief Navigation
Officer, who is expressly
forbidden from issuing
them except on production
of a permit.

Sa 9

<Kryten>
Today remembered that I haven't visited my spare
heads for several months. I guess it's true what
Mr Lister's always saying – that you forget your
head if it isn't screwed on.

Sunday 10

 **Monday**

> **\<Rimmer, Arnold J\>**
> **LISTER'S DAY:**
> Slobbing in the morning, followed by slobbing in the afternoon. Then a bit of a snooze before the main evening slob.

 **Tuesday**

> **\<Lister\>**
> **Smeg off, Rimmer!**

13 **Wednesday**

Thursday 14

<Kryten>
Pursued my artistic studies, which are coming on
apace. Today, I completed my first landscape:

Friday 15

<Cat>
I'm looking nice,
My hair's nice,
My face is nice,
My suit is nice,
I'm looking really nice!

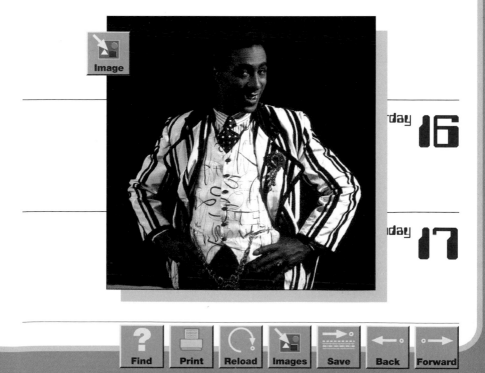

day **16**

day **17**

Monday

> **\<Lister\>**
> Trapped in timewarp.
>
> **\<Kryten\>**
> But I think I have figured a way out.

 Tuesday

> **\<Lister\>**
> Trapped in timewarp.
>
> **\<Kryten\>**
> But I think I have figured a way out.

 Wednesday

> **\<Lister\>**
> Trapped in timewarp.
>
> **\<Kryten\>**
> But I think I have figured a way out.
>
> You must write a sign for our past selves to read,
> warning us to avoid the Stasis Leak that is
> affecting this particular spot in the corridor.

Thursday 18

\<Lister\>
Weird sign suddenly appeared from nowhere in corridor. Handwriting's as bad as mine! Am moving closer to read it...

Friday 18

\<Lister\>
Trapped in timewarp.

\<Kryten\>
But I think I have figured a way out.

You must write a sign for our past selves to read, warning us to avoid the Stasis Leak that is affecting this particular spot in the corridor.

On second thoughts, perhaps I had better do it...

Saturday 18

Sunday 29

\<Lister\>
Escaped from timewarp.

25 Monday

<Lister>
Gazpacho Soup Day.
Served hot, of course.

---

26 Tuesday

---

27 Wednesday

Friday **29**

<Rimmer, Arnold J>
Notes for autobiography, chapter entitled
'Adored by Women':

A love letter

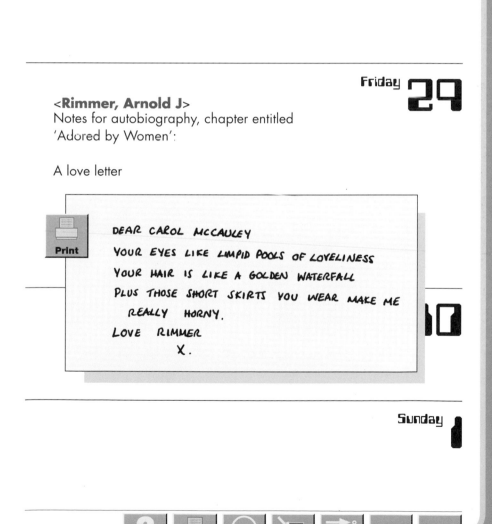

Print

DEAR CAROL MCCAULEY

YOUR EYES LIKE LIMPID POOLS OF LOVELINESS

YOUR HAIR IS LIKE A GOLDEN WATERFALL

PLUS THOSE SHORT SKIRTS YOU WEAR MAKE ME
   REALLY HORNY.

LOVE RIMMER
        X.

Sunday **1**

2 Monday

<Lister>
Intercepted stray Post Pod floating in space. Just our luck – it was junk mail. A circular for the Vid of the Month Club.

3 Tu

4 W

VID OF THE MONTH CLUB

SPECIAL, UNREPEATABLE INTRODUCTORY OFFER!

**The Vid of the Month Club presents
THE TRANSTEMPORAL FILM UNIT'S
new range of FITNESS VIDEOS!
Buy**

The JOAN of ARC Workout Tape

Go for the Burn!

and get

RENE DESCARTES 'Run Your Way Slim'

I Jog Therefore I Am

Absolutely FREE!!!!!

\<Rimmer, Arnold J\>
Lister – only 20 slobbing days till Christmas...

\<Lister\>
Smeg off, Rimmer!

\<Kryten\>
Ah yes, Christmas. That magical time of year
when families come together to eat, drink and
irritate the heck out of one another. I must make
preparations...I wonder what space weevil tastes
like stuffed with chestnuts?

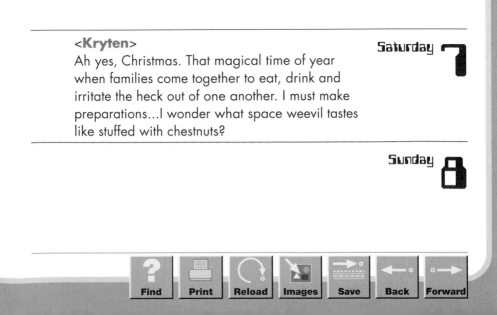

9 Monday

<Holly>
$E=MC^2$, therefore $QxL-P=R^3$, where Fireball $= XL^5$...

10 Tuesday

<Rimmer, Arnold J>
What I want for Christmas (1)

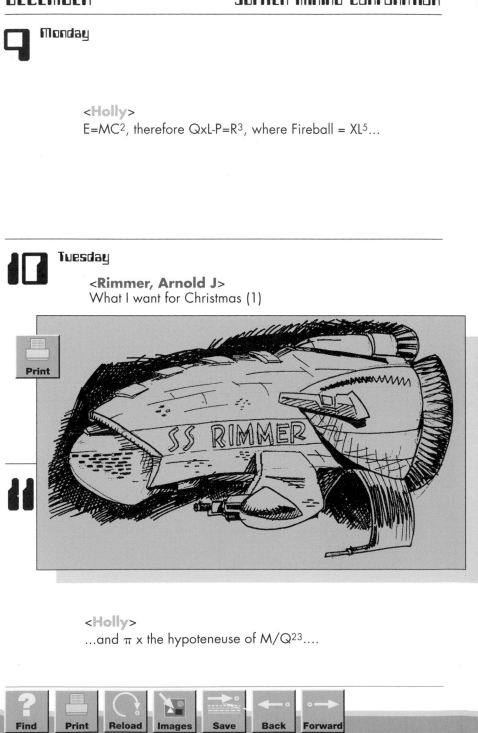

<Holly>
...and π x the hypoteneuse of M/Q^{23}....

Thursday 12

<Cat>
What I want for Christmas…

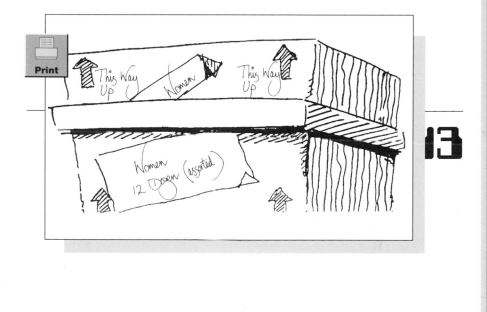

13

<Holly>

Saturday 14

$X + K^4\text{-}TJ\ H^{00}KER = MC^3 \times A$. So basically…I'd say gas mark 8 for about 15 minutes per lb.

<Kryten>
Thank you, Holly

Sunday 15

<Holly>
Though less for a fan assisted oven.

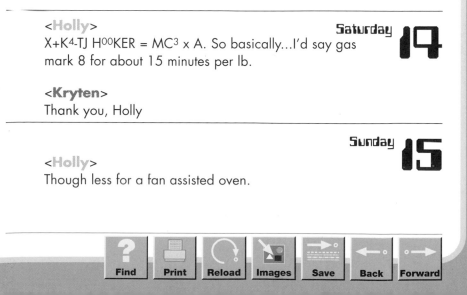

Monday

<Holly>
Good news for Dave. I've located a
frozen turkey in stasis that's only 3 million
years past its eat by date.

Tuesday

<Lister>
Another year nearly over and it still looks like I'm the last
human in the universe...

Wednesday

<Lister>
BEING LAST LIVING HUMAN BEING

Pros - Don't have to queue for bus
Can leave toilet seat up
Am best guitarist in universe
Unlikely now to be called for jury service

Cons - No buses
No women
3 million years between legovers

\<Kryten\>

Here is a drawing of what I'd like for Christmas...

9 780434 003709

Although, obviously, I'd prefer a green one.

\<Rimmer, Arnold J\>

What I want for Christmas (2):

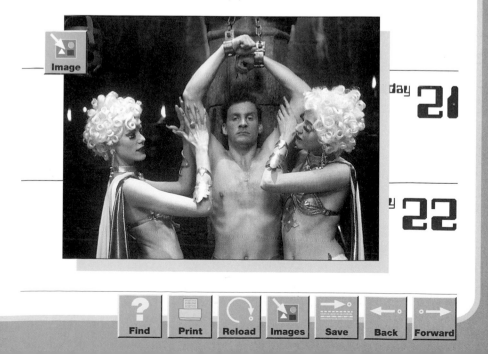

23 Monday

24

Christmas Eve

\<Lister\>
What I want for Christmas...

25 Wednesday

Christmas Day

\<Lister\>
Quiet day by the monitor. Watched vid of that classic
Christmas film *Alien vs. Mary Poppins; The Bitch Is Back.*

\<Rimmer, Arnold J\>
I went carolling.

\<Lister\>
The Space Corps anthem is NOT a carol, smeghead!!!

Boxing Day   Thursday  26

<Cat>
Hey – any turkey left?

Friday  27

<Kryten>
Turkey sandwiches.

Saturday 28

<Kryten>
Turkey sandwiches.

Sunday 29

<Kryten>
Turkey sandwiches.

Find   Print   Reload   Images   Save   Back   Forward

 **30** Monday

---

31 Tuesday

<Kryten>
Vol-au-vents de dindon.

 Wednesday

<Lister>
<Rimmer, Arnold J>
<Cat>
<Kryten>
<Holly>
H A P P Y   N E W   Y E A R !!!!!!!!

Image

Print

Look Out Earth —

The Slimes coming home !!!

Find   Print   Reload   Images   Save   Back   Forward

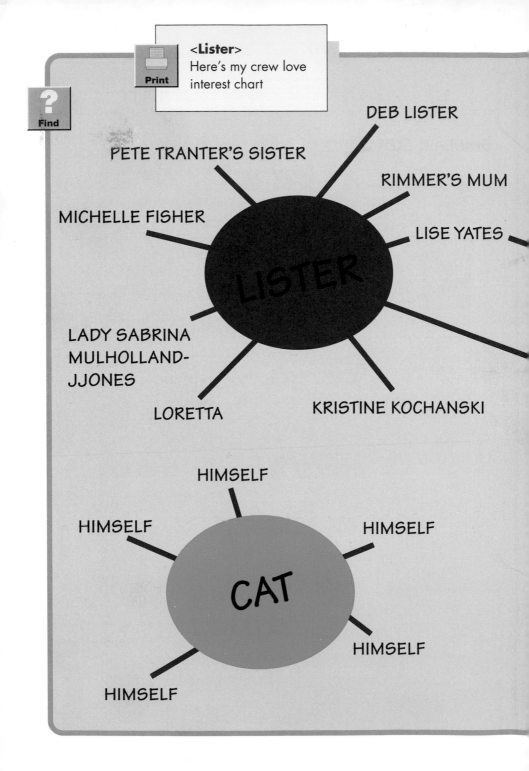

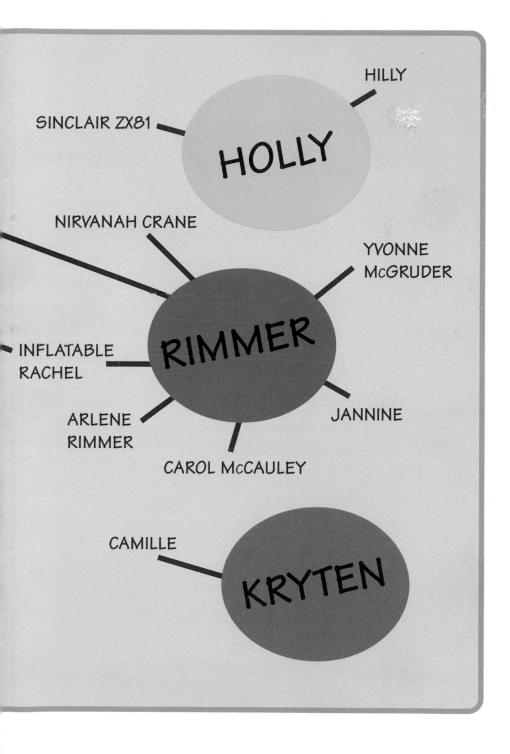

HILLY

SINCLAIR ZX81

HOLLY

NIRVANAH CRANE

YVONNE McGRUDER

RIMMER

INFLATABLE RACHEL

JANNINE

ARLENE RIMMER

CAROL McCAULEY

CAMILLE

KRYTEN

SERVICE INFORMATION
RED DWARF LOG No.1996

Official Red Dwarf Fan Clubs:
UK: 40 Pitford Road, Woodley, Reading, Berks RG5 4QF
Ireland: 67 Rafters Road, Drimnagh, Dublin 12, Ireland
Australia: PO Box 1044, Bundoora, Victoria 3083, Australia
USA: PO Box 13097, Coyote, CA 95013, USA

Video
Series 1-6, plus Smegs Ups and Smeg Outs are available from BBC Video.
Mail order hotline: 0181 576 2236

Books
Three Red Dwarf novels *(Infinity Welcomes Careful Drivers, Better than Life*
and *Last Human)* are available from Penguin (mail order: 0181 899 4036)
and also as audiobooks from Laughing Stock (0171 498 0102) and
Polygram (0181 910 5000). Other books are *The Official Companion*
(Titan: 0171 620 0200); *The Making of Red Dwarf* (Penguin); *The Quiz Book*
(Penguin); *The Programme Guide* (Virgin: 0181 968 7554) and *The Man
Behind the Rubber Mask* (Penguin).

Clothing and accessories
Jackets, sweatshirts, t-shirts, baseball caps and mugs are available from
Distribution Network (mail order: 0181 543 1231); pewter badges and
dogtags from Alchemy Carta (01533 824824).

A range of Red Dwarf posters and calendars (Scandecor: 01480 456395),
greetings cards (Portico Designs: 01272 478870) and model kits
(Sevans Models: 01373 826350) are also available.

SPACE FACTS
GANYMEDE

Plexi-glass dome houses large settlement. Notable only for its Holiday Inn, popular with honeymooners.

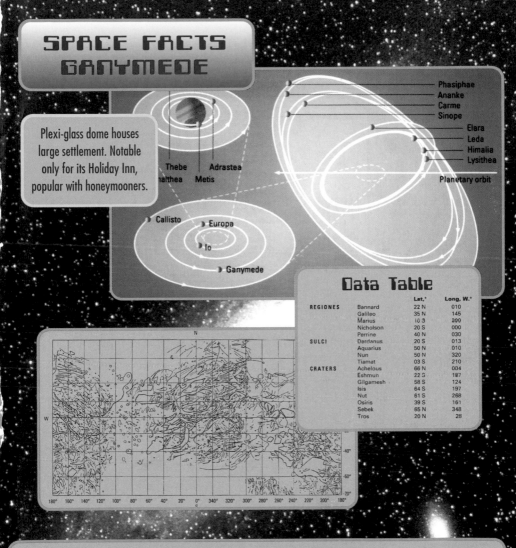

Thebe Adrastea
malthea Metis

Callisto Europa Io Ganymede

Phasiphae
Ananke
Carme
Sinope
Elara
Leda
Himalia
Lysithea

Planetary orbit

Data Table

		Lat.°	Long. W.°
REGIONES	Bannard	22 N	010
	Galileo	35 N	145
	Marius	10 3	200
	Nicholson	20 S	000
	Perrine	40 N	030
SULCI	Dardanus	20 S	013
	Aquarius	50 N	010
	Nun	50 N	320
	Tiamat	03 S	210
CRATERS	Achelous	66 N	004
	Eshmun	22 G	187
	Gilgamesh	58 S	124
	Isis	64 S	197
	Nut	61 S	268
	Osiris	39 S	161
	Sebek	65 N	348
	Tros	20 N	28

Satellites of Jupiter

Name	Distance from Jupiter, km	Orbital period days	Orbital incl., °	Orbital ecc.	Diameter, km	Density, water=1	Escape vel., km/s	Mean opp. mag.
Metis	127,900	0.290	0	0	40	3?	0.02?	17.4
Adrastea	128,980	0.298	0	0	26 x 20 x 16	3?	0.01?	18.9
Amalthea	181,300	0.498	0.45	0.003	262 x 146 x 143	3?	0.16?	14.1
Thebe	221,900	0.675	0.9	0.013	110 x 90	3?	0.8?	15.5
Io	421,600	1.769	0.04		3660 x 3637 x 3631	3.55	2.56	5.0
Europa	670,900	3.551	0.47	0.009	3130	3.04	2.10	5.3
Ganymede	1,070,00	7.155	0.21	0.002	5268	1.93	2.78	4.6
Callisto	1,880,000	16.689	0.51	0.007	4806	1.81	2.43	5.6
Leda	11,094,000	238.7	26.1	0.148	10	3?	0.1?	20.2
Himalia	11,480,000	250.6	27.6	0.158	170	3?	0.1?	14.8
Lysithea	11,720,000	269 ?	29.0	0.107	24	3?	0.01?	18.4
Elara	11,737,000	259.7	24.8	0.207	90	3?	0.05?	16.7
Ananke	21,200,000	631*	147	0.17	20	3?	0.01?	18.9
Carme	22,600,000	692*	164	0.21	30	3?	0.02	18.0
Pasiphaë	23,500,000	735*	145	0.38	36	3?	0.02	17.7
Sinope	23,700,000	758*	153	0.28	28	3?	0.01?	18.3

(* = retrograde)

348,529 ~30

A71

A72

**initial co-ordinates
at year start**

348,529.7
A74.1

PROPOSED ROUTE

actual ROUTE